The Adventures of the Fianna

This story was adapted by author Ann Carroll
and illustrated by Derry Dillon

IRELAND'S BEST KNOWN STORIES
IN A
NUTSHELL

Published 2014
by: In a Nutshell

An Imprint of Poolbeg Press Ltd

123 Grange Hill, Baldoyle
Dublin 13, Ireland

Text © Poolbeg Press Ltd 2014

A catalogue record for this book is available from the British Library.

ISBN 978 1 84223 615 4

Cover design and illustrations by Derry Dillon
Printed by GPS Colour Graphics Ltd, Alexander Road, Belfast BT6 9HP

This book belongs to

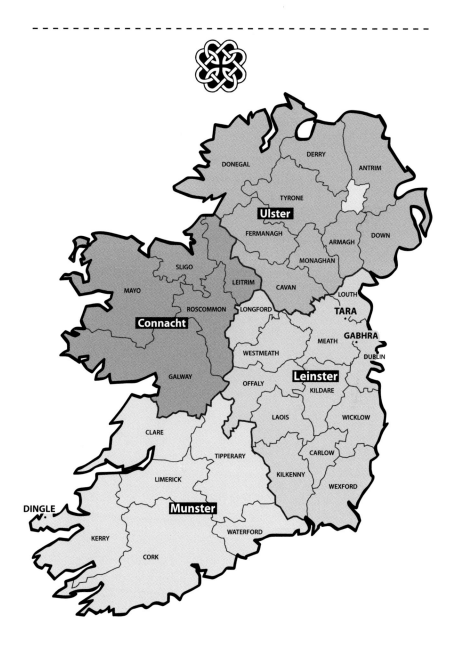

DONEGAL

DERRY

ANTRIM

TYRONE

Ulster

FERMANAGH

ARMAGH

DOWN

MONAGHAN

SLIGO

LEITRIM

CAVAN

MAYO

LOUTH

ROSCOMMON

LONGFORD

TARA

Connacht

MEATH

GABHRA

WESTMEATH

DUBLIN

GALWAY

OFFALY

Leinster

KILDARE

LAOIS

WICKLOW

CLARE

TIPPERARY

CARLOW

LIMERICK

KILKENNY

WEXFORD

DINGLE

Munster

KERRY

WATERFORD

CORK

Also in the Nutshell series

A Band of Warriors

Long, long ago, when Conn of the Hundred Battles was High King of Ireland, a group of young men was becoming famous. They roamed the land and were known as the Fianna – or Band of Warriors.

To join the band, a youth had to prove he could run like the wind, race silently through an autumn forest, endure pain without stopping, jump over high branches and defend himself against the spears of nine warriors. Besides all that, he had to know by heart the twelve books of Bardic Poetry.

The Fate of Cumhall

The Fianna's leader was Cumhall, and he was
the bravest and the best of warriors. But one
man held a grudge against him because his
daughter, Muirne, had fallen in love with him
and they had eloped.

"It's not right!" the angry father told the High King. "I gave no permission for her to marry. He has stolen her from me and must be punished!"

So Cumhall was outlawed by the High King.

Anyone could declare war on an outlaw and one of the Fianna, Aedh Mac Mórna, saw his chance to take over as leader. He challenged Cumhall to battle and killed him, but not without losing the sight of one eye. From then on he was known as Goll Mac Mórna, for 'goll' in Irish means blind.

Cumhall left a son and daughter. Muirne never let them forget their father and was always telling stories of his daring deeds as leader of the Fianna. One day, his son Fionn thought, I will be their leader!

Fionn's Boyhood

In childhood he was trained by the wise man, Finnegas, to be a great warrior. And he himself became the wisest person in the world when he was cooking the Salmon of Knowledge for his master. The first to taste the fish would know everything, so Fionn was warned not to taste it. But he burned his thumb on the hot skin and immediately put it in his mouth, and so by accident tasted it first.

By now Conn had died and the High King was Cormac Mac Airt. He heard of the Fianna's great deeds and was very impressed.

I've so many enemies, he thought. I and my palace at Tara could do with some protection!

So Goll and the Fianna agreed to fight for Cormac and protect Tara from Samhain to Bealtaine (Hallowe'en to spring) in return for gold. They were free to hunt during summer and early autumn.

But they didn't do a great job. Every
Samhain a particularly nasty fire-breathing
dragon sent the warriors to sleep and burned
down the palace.

After a couple of years Cormac got fed up.
"Why am I paying you?" he asked the warriors.
"All you do is snore away while Tara burns!
I'm sick of rebuilding it."

Fionn heard the story and said to himself:
Time for me to make my mark.

And so he travelled to Tara and when the monster cast a spell over the warriors and they all nodded off, he stayed awake by prodding his forehead with his spear whenever his eyes started closing. With the same spear he killed the dragon and when the Fianna woke they were overjoyed. He was accepted as their leader, even by Goll Mac Mórna, and even though he was still a boy.

Conan The Bald

The Fianna had many heroes and one of these was Conan Maol (Baldy) Mac Mórna – a brother of Goll. Conan looked nothing like a fighter, being short and wide and totally bald.

He was also inclined to be very rude.

"You're so ugly!" he would say to a plain woman.

"No, I'm not! That's not me!" she would shout indignantly. "That's you looking at your reflection!"

Then there'd be an argument about which of them was the ugliest. It was an argument Conan always won.

In battle his enemies tended to make mistakes about him. "Look at him!" they'd say. "Sure he's so short and enormous he can hardly move. I nearly feel sorry for him."

But it was his enemies who ended up dead. Conan Maol was so brave even the Sidhe – people from the Otherworld with magic power – loved to see him fight. In one battle he had all the skin stripped from his back and was in great pain, but the Sidhe took pity on him and put a sheep's skin against him, where it quickly became part of his own body.

From then on he had a very woolly back, which did nothing for his looks. Most likely he had to get sheared every so often. Now and again a foolish enemy BAAAAAAED at him and did not live to BAAAAAA again!

(If he'd done much jumping they'd have called him a Woolly Jumper, but luckily for his enemies he was too busy fighting to jump very often.)

The Fastest Man in Ireland

Caoilte Mac Rónáin was another hero. He was the fastest runner in Ireland, possibly the fastest runner on the face of the earth. Once, to win a bet, he ran from Dingle in Kerry to Tara in Meath in less than a day. He was also a great storyteller and those listening around the campfire were spellbound.

But his greatest gift was that he could communicate with animals and make them do his bidding.

One time, Fionn had a row with the High King who threw him into a dungeon at Tara. Fionn didn't try to escape.

If I break out, he thought, Cormac will always be my enemy and will no longer pay the Fianna. I must think of a way to win back his friendship.

While Fionn was thinking, Caoilte came to Tara looking to free his leader.

"I'll release him with no bad feeling on one condition," the High King told him. "You must bring back alive two of every kind of wild animal and bird that lives in Ireland."

Caoilte roamed the land and returned with ducks, geese, swans, ravens, eagles and every other type of bird. Along with these he brought wild horses, foxes, boars, rabbits, hares and all kinds, possibly even a couple of snakes (for this was before Saint Patrick). The din they made approaching Tara was horrible.

Most of the animals didn't want to be in Tara. They wanted to be back home and protested loudly all the way up the hill to the palace, giving out to Caoilte in their own language about the inconvenience. But because they liked him they went with him.

Cormac Mac Airt couldn't stand the racket. All the quacking and howling and shrieking and whinnying gave him a terrible headache. And everyone in the palace was shouting at him, trying to be heard above the noise, wanting an explanation.

Instead he ran in a most unkingly way to
where Fionn was imprisoned, grabbed him by
the arm and rushed him out the door of Tara.

"Here he is!" he roared at Caoilte. "Get rid of that brigade of lunatics!"

The animals, sensing an insult, took umbrage and created even more of a row.

Fionn told the High King, "He'll send them home if I have a promise that nothing changes between us."

By now the High King was a wreck and would have promised anything. "Yes, yes," he said. "Just make them go away."

So Caoilte spoke a few words and the animals flew, galloped, loped, slithered, rushed and trundled off to their various homes and things went back to normal between the High King and Fionn.

The Battle of Gabhra

Cormac ruled for forty years, paying protection money to the Fianna. Then one day, when he was having his dinner, he choked on a salmon bone and died.

His son, Cairbre, was the next High King and, when he saw the palace accounts, he decided at once that the Fianna were getting no more payment from him.

I don't need their protection, he thought. Fionn is too greedy and has many enemies. I'll raise my own army and fight the Fianna if necessary!

Of course it was necessary, for Fionn felt he'd given good service for many years, risking his own and his men's lives.

"We will not be thrown aside by Cairbre!"
he told the Fianna. "I'll give him one last
chance and send my servant to Tara to collect
the gold still owing to us!"

Instead of paying up, Cairbre killed the servant, and so the great Battle of Gabhra began.

Some say Fionn fought alongside his son Oisín and grandson Oscar. The fighting was fierce and Oscar managed to kill Cairbre but died of his own wounds some time later.

Fionn was an old man at this stage, yet fought bravely, killing many. But then he found himself surrounded by five of the enemy, cut off from his friends. Attacked from all sides, he put up a great fight but in the end was slain.

Only twenty warriors altogether survived the battle. Some say Oisín was one and lived on into old age, when he met Saint Patrick and told him all about the Fianna. Others say Oisín never fought at Gabhra, for he was in Tír na nÓg and only met Patrick on his return, centuries later.

The End of the Fianna

What is true is that the Battle of Gabhra broke
the Fianna forever. The glory days were over.
Yet sometimes on the Hill of Tara when
darkness descends and the air is still, it is
said you can hear the voices of the Fianna
and see their shadows around a ghostly fire.

And, if you listen carefully, everything will go quiet as Caoilte Mac Rónáin tells one of his spellbinding stories.

The End

Word Sounds

(Opinions may differ regarding pronunciation)

Words	Sounds
Cumhall	Cool
Muirne	Mwir-neh
Aedh	Ey (to rhyme with Hey)
Goll	Gowl
Fionn	Fee-un
Finnegas	Fin-eh-gas
Samhain	Sow-in (Sow rhymes with How)
Bealtaine	Be-owl-tin-eh
Maol	Mwale
Sidhe	Shc
Caoilte	Keel-cheh
Cairbre	Car-breh
Gabhra	Gow-rah
Oisin	Usheen

Also available from the **IN A NUTSHELL** series

All you need to know about Ireland's best loved stories in a nutshell

The Story of Newgrange

The Salmon of Knowledge

The Story of Saint Patrick

How Cúchulainn Got His Name

The Children of Lir

The Story of The Giant's Causeway

Granuaile The Pirate Queen

Oisín and Tír na nÓg

The Story of Brian Boru

Deirdre of the Sorrows

Heroes of the Red Branch Knights

If you enjoyed this book from
Poolbeg why not visit our website:

www.poolbeg.com

and get another book delivered straight
to your home or to a friend's home.

All books despatched within 24 hours.

POOLBEG

Why not join our mailing list
at www.poolbeg.com and get some
fantastic offers, competitions,
author interviews and much more?

@PoolbegBooks